*This is
my photo*

My name is

The Story of Rebecca

First published in 2008

Childnames.net
27 Villarea Park, Glenageary, Co. Dublin, Ireland
info@childnames.net
www.childnames.net
Tel +353 87 936 9888

Written by Eithne Diamond and John Gallagher

Illustrations by Inno Minds

Additional illustrative input,
layout and pre-press: Ferret on the Dartboard

Text and illustrations copyright Eithne Diamond and John Gallagher

ISBN 978-1-906326-19-7

Design by DVD
Printed in China by Ming Tai Printing Co Ltd

For Conor and Sadhbh
ED and JG

The Story of Rebecca

Eithne Diamond and John Gallagher

Illustrations: Inno Minds

Childnames.net

Rebecca :

the facts for big people

- The name Rebecca, also spelled Rebekah, is drawn from the Old Testament.

- It probably derives from the Hebrew word *rivka*, meaning to bind, or tie a noose, and it has come to mean captivating, or a captivating personality.

- In the Bible, Rebecca is the mother of Jacob.

- She is notable for bearing a child at an advanced age and in controlling her aging husband's inheritance.

- Rebecca is one of the few female characters that are developed in detail in the Bible.

- Her life is detailed in the Book of Genesis 16, 19–26 and 27. It suggests that women may have exercised significant hidden power in an ancient society that was overwhelmingly male-dominated.

• Our story is inspired by a Biblical account of the young Rebecca, who offers water to an old man and his camels.

• She is rewarded with jewels before marrying the man's employer, Isaac, son of Abraham, the founder the Hebrew nation.

• Many years later she tricks her aging husband into parting with his inheritance, conniving with Jacob, the favourite of her twin sons, to achieve her aim.

• When her plot is discovered after the event, she further connives with her brother, Laban, to shelter Jacob.

• *Rebecca* is the title of one of the foremost books by English novelist, playwright and biographer, Daphne du Maurier.

• Published in 1938 it was filmed by Alfred Hitchcock, winning two Oscars including Best Picture in 1940. A 1997 TV movie remake received an Emmy.

• In Sir Walter Scott's novel *Ivanhoe* (1819), set in 12th century England, Rebecca is the daughter of Isaac of York.

• A 1952 movie of the book starred Elizabeth Taylor as Rebecca.

• The 'Rebecca riots' occurred in Wales between 1839 and 1844, in opposition to tolling of roads.

• The riots began in Carmarthenshire and were named after a Biblical reference.

• Rebecca Storm has starred in leading stage musicals including 'Evita,' 'Bloodbrothers,' 'Les Miserables' and 'Cats.'

• Rebecca Miller, author of a recently-published book, is a daughter of playwright Arthur Miller. One of her films, 'The Ballad of Jack and Rose' starred her husband Daniel Day-Lewis.

• Rebecca St James is an Australian-born, Grammy award-winning Gospel singer.

• Rebecca Loos is a Spanish-born model and former PA to footballer David Beckham.

• Rebecca is the name of a town in Georgia, USA.

Rebecca :

the story for little people

O nce there was a girl named Rebecca.

In Rebecca's land there were no cars or bicycles.
Instead her mum and dad walked everywhere.
For really long journeys they travelled by camel taxi.

There was no television. Instead people told
each other stories. Sometimes funny stories,
sometimes scary stories.

Rebecca lived before electricity was discovered.
So every night her mum and dad placed candles
in her room to give light.

There were no showers or sinks or taps. Instead people collected water in large jars from a deep well on the edge of her town.

Poor Rebecca! She didn't have many of the things that you have in your house. Guess what she did have though?

Jewellery! Lots and lots of jewellery.

Rebecca really loved her rings and bracelets.

She wore a ring on every finger.
Sometimes, when she felt like really dressing up, she wore rings on her toes as well!

Rebecca loved jewellery so much that everyone who visited her house brought her new pieces.

"I have even more jewellery than you, mum," she would say.

"Especially since you borrow mine too when I'm not looking," her mum would reply.

One of Rebecca's jobs was to collect water
for her family from a well in the village.

Once, when she was returning from the well,
she noticed an old man sitting on a seat. He looked
very tired and poor. Rebecca knew that he had
travelled a long way because a camel stood by his side.

People were passing by and ignoring the old man
and his camel.

"Look at that wretched old man," they laughed.

"I have not had a drink for three days,"
the old man said.

"I have not had a drink for three weeks,"
the camel said.

Rebecca knew that a camel can live for a long time
without water. Their home is in the desert.
When they find some water they drink a lot and
store it in a hump on their back.

Rebecca offered the old man a drink.
Next she gave water to the camel.

Then she went back to the well to collect more water
for her family.

At the well there was lot of activity.

Some people were selling
coffee and biscuits.
Others were selling rugs
and blankets.

"Would you like to buy new sandals?
Half price today!" a shopkeeper said,
as Rebecca walked past.

When Rebecca returned to the spot where
the old man had been sitting, he was gone.
A handsome prince stood there instead!
He had not one, but two camels.

The prince spoke to Rebecca.

"You helped me when I was
tired and thirsty.
Now I will give you
a reward," he said.

He opened a large bag on the camel's back.

From it he took a fistful of jewellery that sparkled
like gold and silver in the sun.

There were necklaces and bracelets, bangles and
rings, brooches and anklebands, diamonds and
rubies, emeralds and sapphires.

He offered Rebecca more jewellery than she had
ever seen before.

Rebecca invited the prince to meet her family.

Her mum was very surprised to see Rebecca's new jewellery. She was delighted when the prince said that his second camel was a gift for her family.

"Oh! Cool," Rebecca said. "Now we won't have to wait ages for a camel taxi to arrive."

Then they all had a big feast outside.
Even the camels had some cake and lemonade!

When Rebecca told her mum the story of how the prince had been disguised as a very poor man her mum was even more surprised.

"You learned something very important today.
If you are kind to others they will be kind to you," her mum said.

"Oh, and from now on I will be the one to borrow your jewellery!" she laughed.

What's in a name?
— more facts for big people

- When actress Betty Joan Perske was given the screen name Lauren Bacall one of the most popular first names for girls of recent decades was created.

- *The name Keira did not exist until the 21st century, except as a misspelling!*

- It is soaring up the baby name charts due to the success of UK-born actress Keira Knightly. She changed the spelling from Kiera to avoid mispronunciation in Hollywood.

- *Today there are thousands of first names. Even the most popular names may account for only 2–3% of the overall total.*

- There were far fewer names in previous centuries. Baptism registers in the UK during the second half of the 16th century record that one in five boys was named William.

- *During the second half of the 18th century, just three names – Elizabeth, Mary and Anne – accounted for 57% of all girls born in the UK.*

- As recently as the early 20th century, some first names were so common in Ireland that a second 'first' name was added for identification, often based on a parent's first name: hence the character Paidín Mike in Synge's famous play 'The Playboy of the Western World.'

- *In the north of England, until the late 19th century, many people relied on multiple names to convey family identity – for instance, Tom o'Dick o'Mary's.*

- Today's parents increasingly use original and inventive first names as a means of conveying identity and 'brand' to their children.

- *Back in the 16th century, however, the Council of Trent ruled that Catholics could name their children only after canonised saints or angels.*

- During the same period, in Britain and USA the Puritans insisted that only names from the Bible were valid. They later allowed names such as Livewell and Safe-on-high.

- *Without any edicts, the double name John Paul suddenly became popular in Ireland after the Pope visited the country in 1979.*

- From the 13th to the 15th century it was common to give the same name to more than one child in a family: the second would be known, for example, as John the younger.

- *The name Jesus is highly popular in Spanish-speaking countries, but considered sacrilegious in much of northern and central Europe.*

- Changing a person's name was once a grave offence. Records in the English city of Rochester state that on Oct 15th, 1515, an Agnes Sharpe 'voluntarily changed the name of her infant son … for which she submitted penance.'

- *Many names still originate from religious history, such as Cate, Katie and Kate from Saint Catherine.*

- How a name is spelled can have religious links also. Sarah is a favourite for Christians, while Sara is preferred by Muslims.

- *The popular boy's name Aaron emerged as a variation of the Biblical Aron, thanks to Elvis Aaron Presley.*

- A name from Irish legend, Conor, has recently become popular internationally but it is often spelled Connor, which denotes a surname in Ireland!

- *Lawrence (Latin), Chloe (Greek literature) and Victoria (history) are examples of other sources for names.*

- Then there's Jack! It seems to have emerged from nowhere – but perhaps from Jankin, a version of John – to become the ubiquitous name of fairy tales and a highly-popular first name.

- *Name 'globalisation' gives us monikers like Tanya, Brooklyn and Chelsea.*

- The general decrease in formality – nobody is now known as Mr, or Mrs, Jones – leads parents to seek ever more imaginative and unique names.

- *Names popular in one country may hardly exist elsewhere. Ever heard of Seren or Cerys? Both are Top 20 names for girls in Wales.*

- Copying celebrities is popular. In 2000 Sonny Sandoval, singer with American group POD, mentioned on MTV that he had named his daughter Nevaeh ('Heaven' backwards). By 2005 more than 3,000 girls were given the name each year in the USA.

- *Finally, before opting for the latest new fab name, it would be both wise and humorous to take a listen to the Johnny Cash song 'A Boy Named Sue.'*

Christening ... Birthdays ... Christmas ...
We'll post your order to you!

Order books from this series
for postal delivery
to **anywhere in the world**.

- **Credit card bookings**:
  click the 'Purchase' link on *www.childnames.net* and follow the steps.

- **Order by post**:
  check the postage costs to your country and the accepted payment methods
  on *www.childnames.net*, then forward the total amount, with the name of
  the book(s) required and your postal address, to:

  Childnames.net, 27 Villarea Park, Glenageary, Co Dublin, Ireland.

A personalised 'My name is ...' poster for your child!

- visit *www.childnames.net*
- click on 'Posters'
- select from a range of illustrations ...
- and follow the links.

Please note:

This service is available by
mail order only (posters are
not available in bookshops).